The Dad's Guide
to Pregnancy

J. Bird

J. Bird Productions
Cumming, Georgia

THE DAD'S GUIDE TO PREGNANCY

By J. Bird

Published by J.Bird Productions
562 Lakeland Plaza
Suite 182
Cumming GA, 30040
(770) 643-1000

First printing October 2002

ISBN 0-9710418-0-6

Cover and illustrations by Michael Gaffney
Young Creative Associates, Inc.
Hendersonville, North Carolina

Printed in the USA by Faith Printing Company, Inc., Taylors, South Carolina

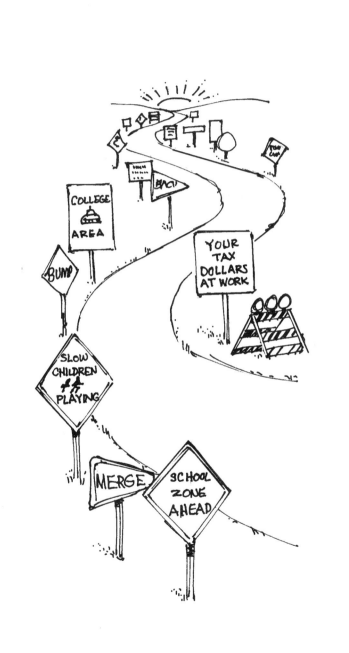

Foreword

As a performer and emcee for many years, I constantly have a microphone in my hand and a room or auditorium full of people gazing at me hoping something humorous will fall from my lips.

Instead of the same stale jokes of many a master of ceremonies, I've always relied upon personal experience—you know, the things we all go through and sometimes fuss about—to connect me with my audience. Because, for some reason, when we stand back and listen to what another poor soul is going through or has been through we can find it very—ah, how can I say this gently—funny.

This book is a recounting and embellishment of some of that real life material which now I too can find funny. Laugh at me as I recall and reflect on those times and attempt to prepare you for what is about to come your way. But, also know that I'm laughing with YOU, because I realize that some of you just have NO idea what you're getting into.

Enjoy the ride.

I. Conception

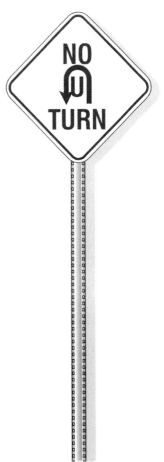

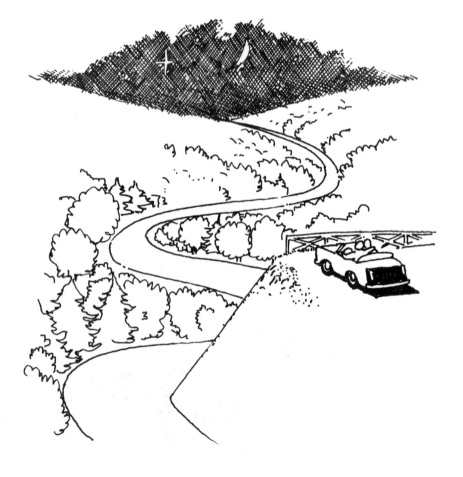

If you're lucky, you're already pregnant and this will just be a humorous little chapter for you to enjoy. If you're not pregnant and you're reading this book—it must mean you are in the thick of what I am about to describe.

There is only one way to get pregnant . . . or is there? I used to think a candlelit dinner for two, a roaring fire, and BINGO!—you and me and the baby makes three. I found out quickly that this method works great on soap operas and for those "Oops, we're pregnant" deals. If you are planning to have a baby, trust me. This method is too easy to work.

After striking out with caviar, your loving wife's research will determine that she can only get pregnant a certain time during her monthly cycle—which upon first consideration sounds reasonable. Right? You say to yourself, "No problem, wine and candles on the 15th, 16th, and 17th of next month."

It's too bad you forgot you had to be out of town the 15th, had a ball game on the 16th, and your mother-in-law comes to visit on the 17th. Another month rolls by.

You plan again to be romantic by the calendar, and just as before, the pressure begins. Not to mention the fact that the beautiful girl you married is quickly becoming a pregnancy expert, reading tons of magazine articles, checking out web sites, and catching up with wives tales I won't even try to describe.

The three-day window, as it is now called at dinner, arrives. Every detail is planned. You hurry through dinner—she looks hard at a glass of wine now because of what it might do to a potential baby. You turn the lights down low. . . Did something happen, or does this feel like a movie script? What happened to spontaneity and foreplay? What's *foreplay?*

You get back over there and do your job!

And, guess what?

No pink stick.

Yep, she's got a new best friend named EPT. The early pregnancy test—accurate nearly 100% the morning after. Wow! Don't you feel like a loser! Swing and a miss, huh, big guy?

The next words from her mouth will live in infamy: "Maybe *you* should see a doctor, honey."

A doctor? Not you! You're virile, full of life, a man's man. Sure, sure, I know. But listen carefully: DON'T STEP IN THIS ONE. Never throw back the simple, even possibly logical statement: "Maybe the trouble is with you." This will set off a chain reaction of emotions you are not going to be in the mood for. *(WARNING: this is one of those comments which could come up from now on whenever even small arguments like "You think I'm fat, don't you," break out.)*

So remember, just humor her and beg for another month or two of trying. Try to relax and let it happen.

The next little discovery by your evolving pregnancy Einstein will be the dreaded ovulation tester stick. Oh, yeah, it's a natural progression. They have them on the shelf right next to the EPT so they know that, should the need arise, she'll see 'em! Now the monthly cycle method as previously described will seem like your honeymoon compared to the clinical, time-sensitive moments to follow.

You've just returned home after a difficult day at work. Your home life has been a bit strained over the past several months, and you are just plain tired. Sitting on the potty with a set of directions and a pink stick is your love goddess. "Honey, get undressed," is her greeting which, to tell you the truth, in college you would have dreamed about. But for some reason, at this moment, you just feel cheap.

After you strain to do the deed, she assumes a new "afterglow position" lying on her back both feet straight up.

"What a babe," you think to yourself as you head to the john.

No EPT pink stick next morning, but she warns you the trick will not be repeated that evening, because you have to save up to get your count back up. Is this the girl you married? How did she get to be the mad scientist she is today? How did you get demoted to sperm donor?

Smile through it, my friend. Pick up some flowers on the way home, take her out to dinner. You won't have to perform tonight!

Next morning—try to be romantic. Kiss her and hold her before you get out of bed. Tell her you love her and that she's beautiful—tonight could be the night.

Stay with it. It *will* happen—all in God's time. And, trust me, when it's all over with and you're holding that little treasure in your arms, it all will have been worth it!

II. So, You're Pregnant!
The first month

Yeah! Let the fun begin. I hope you have plenty of room on the your credit cards, because even though you will probably be inundated with gifts from family and well wishers, you are about to become *super shopping man!*

Your new mom-to-be will now turn her growing hunger for knowledge towards maternity clothes, baby furniture, and—unfortunately—newer, safer automobiles.

It's all about safety now. Forget about value. She will become a *Consumer Digest* subscriber and begin amassing materials and sources too numerous to be refuted by you, a mere mortal. Face it, you will be out shopping for baby furniture soon, and not just any furniture, mind you—furniture hand built by Ralph Nader himself! And even though you may find what you're looking for at the first giant baby discount store you visit, you will still have to spend countless, precious golf days exploring the one her sister told her about in the next county.

Again, relax. This too shall pass.

You'll see another change in your bride at any moment now. Without advance notice she'll pass through the room with an oversized, frumpy maternity shirt on. Now she's only been pregnant for a few days; but she is so excited, she forgot to tell you she dropped a few gillion bucks on a whole new wardrobe.

Be smart. Tell her the clothes look great and that you doubt she'll ever grow into them. When people don't ask her about her condition or otherwise notice her new attire, she will (although a little let down) change back to normal wife wear for now. But be on the lookout for the subtle "sucker" line of questioning: "Do I look like I'm showing yet, honey?" For, no matter how innocent your response, you will be heading down a road from which there may be no return. Instead, always take a pass on rendering judgment on such issues and allow girlfriends, sisters, and moms to break the news, girl-talk style, of her impending pooch. You are best served with a simple, "I just can't tell, honey, but I see you everyday—I always think you're beautiful." And then, gentlemen, and I can't emphasize this enough, just walk away, change the subject, jump out the window—you get the idea.

Oh, and one last thing here: She will still have some use for you in the bedroom now. Enjoy it, because the pressure is off! You can't do any harm to Junior, and no protection is required. Whoa—what a concept! But do realize this brief moment in time will be just that—*brief*. Morning sickness, bloating, food-bingeing, and burping are on the way, so live it up while you can.

III. The Long Stretch
Two to eight months

Goo goo gah gah—so now you're talking baby talk to your MBA-once-sophisticated Mrs., referring to her as Mommie, and assuming the role of Daddy yourself. Hopefully, you're over the morning sickness phase now. (If not, bear with her. She may go through a rough patch with nausea, but have courage—it won't last but a few weeks.)

Now you begin to say things like, "Don't worry, Mommie. Daddy will put the crib together, paint the nursery, and run the unending marathon of household chores, and still have time to visit that little glitch in the agenda . . .what was it? . . . on yeah, work!

After the initial excitement, I highly recommend finding out the sex of your impending bundle of joy via the ultrasound. They have to run this test anyway, so bring a blank video and insist on a copy. Believe me, it's worth it. Now you, or need I remind you, SHE, can aggressively begin the name game.

This is another process you will want to steer clear of. If the good Lord had wanted men to name their own children, He would have never created women. But, once the decision has been made, you can both begin to refer to her exploding belly by its proper name.

This is also a great way for our mom-to-be to begin the next cycle: "Daddy, little Johnny wants a Whopper with cheese, a milk shake, and, oh yeah, a cheese dip from the Mexican restaurant in Acapulco where we went on our honey moon.

And, guys—find a way to make it happen! An unsuccessful midnight excursion for these demands will net you grief and mourning for many days to come. As long as her OB is not concerned with excessive weight gain, give her whatever will make her happy.

About now, Dr. Spock (as you may be endearingly referring to your informationally deranged student of all things baby) will discover the fetal heart monitor. Similar in every respect to the one the doc pops on her belly each time she visits, with one stark difference—reception. When cool, calm, and collected OB-Gyn-person, adorned with stethoscope, preppy glasses and Rockport sneakers, enters the room and pops the device on your little mom-to-be's tummy, immediately the *pow, pow, pow* of baby's heartbeat is audible. This seemingly simple task is almost impossible to recreate back at home. Sweet Mommie decides, in your absence, to take a moment to spend a little quality time with Junior, and—BAM!— you're getting a 911 page in the middle of a presentation to your biggest client. You bow out gracefully, dial her up to hear the words: "_____ (insert *child's name from name game above*) doesn't have a heartbeat!"

Your blood runs cold, you count the moments as she races to the OB's office only to find that everything is fine with baby. The problem is most likely with your fetal monitor, which cost about 1/100th of what the doc's cost, and for some reason, *doesn't work as well.*

There may be another explanation for your monitor not registering any sound: It's difficult for nonprofessionals to determine Junior's exact position; and baby's little butt just doesn't *have* a heartbeat!

These are great days, though. Baby starts to kick and move, and you can feel it too. Make sure you do!

Remember, this is the longest stretch of the pregnancy. The time from one month to eight months will sometimes seem like eternity, but there is much to do to occupy your time and her brain.

IV. The Final Days
The ninth month

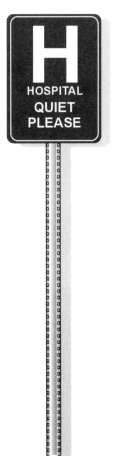

Whoever thought of the idea for the Goodyear blimp must have been staring at his wife during the ninth month of her pregnancy. Up until now she has been gaining steadily and pooching "cutely." But after week 36 or so—BOOM! She's big, REAL BIG! Maternity clothes that once hung elegantly, showing off a pleasantly rounded little bulge, are now pushed to maximum capacity. Baby, who used to make small tapping movements, now becomes the Karate Kid, punching and kicking poor Mommie like Chuck Norris.

And so much for any hope of even small household chore help. Nope. Now all your whale of a wife can do is beach herself on the couch, or walk around like Fred Sanford with one hand on her back and wish for better days.

Knowing that time is short, you'll also begin those final emergency route and procedure plans and promote Mrs. Right to supervisory status for the emergency broadcasting system. Every phone number and pager number is catalogued; and every possible routine errand stop must be charted and approved with military precision in case the final moment should occur "whilst thou art out and about." A "Honey, don't forget the milk," pager call now becomes a 911 race for the phone! No scenario concerning the arrival time can be allowed to remain unexplored as the baby-watch goes on full alert.

Within mere weeks false labor, or Braxton-Hicks contractions, will send normal life into code red status as you scramble all hands on deck, pack the car, and call the in-laws. . .only to hear the "stand down until further notice" order by the supreme (jumbo) commander.

The time of baby's arrival, based on the phase of the moon and relatives' estimates, dominates every conversation, as the do gooders, wives tale-ers, and well wishers begin to put in their two cents' worth as to actual mission completion dates and times. Any and all family birth dates, anniversaries, and other favorite dates can and will be considered formally, as mission control will wish that no stone remain unturned in this quest for knowledge of Junior's actual day of arrival. New moon, full moon—and even Pat Boone—can and will be consulted. But the end is not yet. . .

The only way to describe labor, *real labor*, is to think about those cuddly teddy bears that stores sell in balloons. You know the ones—give a unique gift, have the store put your teddy bear in a fully blown up balloon. Put a bow around the base, and your fortunate honoree will marvel at not only your thoughtfulness but also at the scientific know-how of the gift wrapper. Well, now imagine all of the air being sucked out of the balloon so that you can actually feel the outline of the teddy bear inside. This is what Mommie's belly will feel like when you place you hand on her bulge.

This is real labor—time to go to the hospital, kiss the anesthesiologist, end-of-the-line kind of labor! When that warm, loving, woman of your dreams starts talking bad about your relatives and conjuring up adjectives formerly reserved for the locker room, and when you can feel Junior's anatomy like the vacuum-enhanced teddy, forget about the time between the contractions—get thyself to a delivery room!

V. The Delivery

Right about now, I hope your Mrs. is perched firmly in the stirrups with a warm fuzzy feeling induced by an epidural drip—that she's chattering gayly about how it hasn't been all that difficult, and allowing bone-chilling, off the scale contractions to pass with ease. Only moments before the beloved anesthesiologist's arrival, those same contractions had drawn blood from her grip on your forearm. Relax, it's all over but the crying, because the next sound you'll hear will be your dear sweet baby's first breath of life, love, and liberty!

Don't worry if the doctor's a little late—he really isn't necessary for the whole ordeal to go forward. Your labor and delivery nurses have been through this a million times. They do all the real work. The MD comes in at the end with a catcher's mitt, and—BOOM!—you owe him three grand!

Another thing about these OB-Gyn doctors, they seem to be obsessed with the Dad cutting the cord. Sure, I did it—but there was no real thrill to it. I just wonder, when I finally decide to have that vasectomy, if the doc will be *as* enthusiastic about my wife cutting *that* cord?

Anyway, when baby finally does manage to make it out into the real world, there is a huge to-do with measurements and towels. The kid is screaming bloody murder, but they tell me this is a *good* thing! Now Mommie's crying, baby's crying, Grandma's crying and, to tell the truth, you'll be crying too! Exhaustion, joy, pride, and fear of the hospital bill, all wash away with salty tears as they place the most beautiful girl (or boy) in all the world safely on Mommie's chest. Ten little fingers and ten little toes, Grandma's lungs, and Mommie's nose. What a relief!

This moment doesn't last—take a picture!

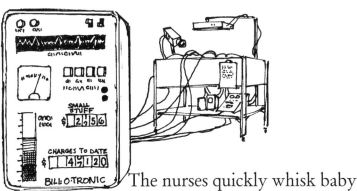

The nurses quickly whisk baby away and install an electronic tracking device on one little leg. They claim it's modern technology, and an alarm will sound should someone leave with the wrong baby. I'm supposed to be comforted by this, but for some reason I can't help but think back to the day when my little (presumed) brother came home from the hospital all those years ago—kinda makes you wonder, doesn't it?

I don't believe them anyway. I think the real reason for this baby "Lojack" is so every time they bring Mommie a Tylenol, all they have to do is scan the kid's ankle and—BOOM!—$20 shows up on my bill.

The first night or two is a bit scary when it's your first baby, because you're not even sure which end to diaper, let alone breastfeed.

All night long, you catch yourself checking to make sure Baby's OK. And, speaking of diapers, you can imagine wet ones, but nothing I can write here will prepare you for what comes out of that little fanny for the first few days! It's normal, but it doesn't seem normal. Again, trust me. Soon Junior's BM will be just the right color and consistency—whatever that is!

About the time you change the third diaper, the doc drops by and pronounces that Mommie is fine, Baby is fine, and you, Sir, are released! Wow—$10K in less than 48 hours. Reminds me of a Vegas trip I took after college.

You put Mommie in the car, briefly study instructions on proper installation of a car seat, strap Baby in the back, and drive off into a life that will never be the same! I'm not talking about maybe for a year or so either— from the moment you pull out of the driveway and forever, my friend.

You will arrive home to a house full of in-laws, and perhaps for the only time in your life, you'll be glad they are there. You see, a newborn is a 24-hour a day job. And the sounds, odors, and discharges that are emitted from that tiny little bundle make it highly desirable to have a seasoned expert on hand for as long as possible! Your mom, her mom, even her sister or distant aunt will be welcome to lend a hand at the 3 am feeding, changing, burping frenzy.

Now it's time to try and rest, find your stride—you're going to be fine. Learn all you can. Love a lot. And pray a lot!

You're the luckiest man alive, and you know what?

So am I!